CONTENTS

A | Answer

1  =

2  =

3  = 3

4  = _____ p

5  = _____ p

6  = 4p _____ p

7   Write the name of this shape.

8 Which pencil is longer?

9 Which day comes after Tuesday?

10  What time is it? _____ o'clock

B | Answer

1 4 + 1 =

2 14 + 1 =

3 24 + 1 =

4 14, 15, 16, 17, ▢

5 7 – 1 =

6 17 – 1 =

7 27 – 1 =

8 27, 26, 25, 24, ▢

9 ▢ + 1 = 4

10 ▢ – 1 = 8

C | Answer

1 Add 7 and 1.

2 Take 1 from 5.

3 The total of 8 and 1 is

4 The difference between 1 and 6 is

5 The sum of 1 and 9 is

6 3 is 1 more than

7 Subtract 1 from 9.

8 4 minus 1 is

9 1 less than 8 is

10 1 plus 6 is

Schofield&Sims

Mental Arithmetic
Introductory Book

Name

THE LANGUAGE OF MATHS

Addition words

+	the plus sign, for 'add' (2 + 1 = 3)
addition	counting up or finding the sum of two or more numbers (3 add 3 = 6)
altogether	to find how many there are 'altogether', add them all up (10 + 2 + 3 = 15, so there are 15 altogether)
greater than	bigger or more than (4 greater than 5 = 9)
increase	if something is increased you have more of it. Increase 3 by 2 and you get 5.
more than	'6 more than 3' is the same as '6 and then 3 more' (6 more than 3 = 9)
plus	add, also shown as '+' (8 plus 8 = 16 or 8 + 8 = 16)
sum	to find the sum, add up all the numbers (the sum of 2 and 4 = 6)
total	'count' or 'add' (the total of 4, 2 and 3 = 9)

How many more than 3 is 5? Answer: 2

Subtraction words

−	the minus sign, for 'subtract' or 'take away' (4 − 2 = 2)
difference	to find the difference between numbers, compare them. There are two ways to find the difference between 8 and 3. Count on from the smaller number 3 to the larger number 8 or write down the larger amount and take the smaller amount away from it. (The difference between 8 and 3 is 5.)
fewer than	less than (3 fewer than 7 is 4)
less than	fewer than, or not as many (4 less than 5 is 1)
minus	take away (8 minus 5 = 3 or 8 − 5 = 3)
subtraction	'taking away' – the answer is the number you have left (You have 6 eggs. You subtract 2. You have 4 left.)
take away	subtract or minus. Sometimes '6 minus 4' will be written as 'take 4 from 6'. Write down the 6 first so that you can take 4 away from it. (6 − 4 = 2 or 6 take away 4 = 2)

What is left when you take 2 from 4? Answer: 2

Multiplication words

×	the multiplication sign, for 'multiply' or 'times' (4 × 2 = 8)
multiplication	a quick way to add up equal sets
multiply	to times one number by another. 2 × 6 means '2 multiplied by 6' or '2 times 6' (multiply 2 by 6)
times	can mean 'multiplied by' (4 times 2 is 8 or 4 × 2 = 8)

Division words

÷	the division sign, for 'divide by' (9 ÷ 3 = 3)
dividing	splitting things into equal groups. You can split 6 into 2 equal groups, with 3 in each. (6 ÷ 2 = 3 or divide 6 by 2 = 3)
share	another way of 'dividing' or 'splitting up' (share 10 coins between 5 people)

How many 2s in 8? Answer: 4

Equals

=	the equals sign, for 'makes' or 'is the same as' (5 add 3 = 8 or 5 add 3 is the same as 8 or 5 add 3 makes 8)

Fractions

half ($\frac{1}{2}$)	divide something into two equal pieces, and each piece is called a half
quarter ($\frac{1}{4}$)	divide something into four equal pieces, and each piece is called a quarter

*From: **Mental Arithmetic Introductory Book**. Copyright © Schofield & Sims Ltd, 2016. This page may be photocopied after purchase.*

A

Answer

1  + = _____

2  – = _____

3  – ? = 4 _____

4  5p + 2p = _____ p

5 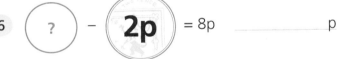 10p – 2p = _____ p

6 ? – 2p = 8p _____ p

7 Write the name of this shape. _____

8 Which ball is heavier? _____

9 Which day comes before Saturday? _____

10  What time is it? _____ o'clock

B

Answer

1 6 + 2 = _____

2 16 + 2 = _____

3 26 + 2 = _____

4 16, 18, 20, 22, ▓ _____

5 5 – 2 = _____

6 15 – 2 = _____

7 25 – 2 = _____

8 25, 23, 21, 19, ▓ _____

9 ▓ + 2 = 4 _____

10 ▓ – 2 = 8 _____

C

Answer

1 Add 8 and 2. _____

2 Take 2 from 9. _____

3 The total of 6 and 2 is _____

4 The difference between 2 and 8 is _____

5 The sum of 2 and 9 is _____

6 4 is 2 more than _____

7 Subtract 2 from 5. _____

8 3 minus 2 is _____

9 2 less than 6 is _____

10 2 plus 7 is _____

Schofield & Sims

A · Answer

1 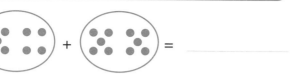 + = _____

2 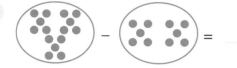 – = _____

3 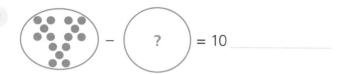 – ? = 10 _____

4  5p + 10p = _____ p

5  20p – 10p = _____ p

6 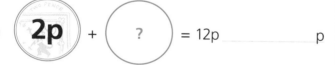 2p + ? = 12p _____ p

7  Write the name of this shape. _____

8 Which glass is full? _____

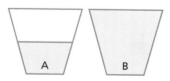

9 Which day comes after Monday? _____

10  What time is it? _____ o'clock

B · Answer

1 3 + 10 = _____

2 13 + 10 = _____

3 23 + 10 = _____

4 13, 23, 33, 43, ▨ _____

5 11 – 10 = _____

6 21 – 10 = _____

7 31 – 10 = _____

8 51, 41, 31, 21, ▨ _____

9 ▨ + 10 = 46 _____

10 ▨ – 10 = 27 _____

C · Answer

1 Add 10 and 3. _____

2 Take 10 from 19. _____

3 The total of 10 and 5 is _____

4 The difference between 15 and 10 is _____

5 The sum of 10 and 6 is _____

6 12 is 10 more than _____

7 Subtract 10 from 18. _____

8 11 minus 10 is _____

9 10 is 4 less than _____

10 10 plus 7 is _____

A
Answer

1  =

2  =

3  = 2

4 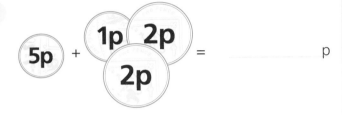 = ____ p

5  = ____ p

6 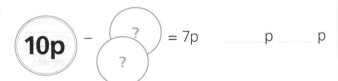 = 7p   ____ p   ____ p

7  Write the name of this shape.

8 Which pencil is shorter?

9 Which day comes before Friday?

10  What time is it?   ____ o'clock

B
Answer

1   6 + 4 =

2   16 + 4 =

3   46 + 4 =

4   26, 36, 46, 56, ▢

5   10 – 3 =

6   20 – 3 =

7   30 – 3 =

8   67, 57, 47, 37, ▢

9   ▢ + 5 = 10

10   10 – ▢ = 9

C
Answer

1   Add 3 and 7.

2   Take 9 from 10.

3   The total of 8 and 2 is

4   The difference between 5 and 10 is

5   The sum of 4 and 6 is

6   10 is 3 more than

7   Subtract 8 from 10.

8   10 minus 1 is

9   6 is 4 less than

10   2 plus 8 is

SECTION 1 | Test 5

A | Answer

1 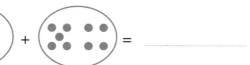 = _____

2 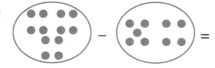 = _____

3  = 3 _____

4 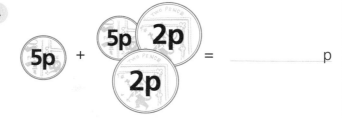 = _____ p

5 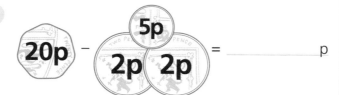 = _____ p

6 = £1 £ _____

7  Write the name of this shape. _____

8 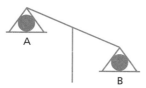 Which ball is lighter? _____

9 Which day comes after Sunday? _____

10  What time is it? _____ o'clock

B | Answer

1 $7 + 9 =$ _____

2 $17 + 9 =$ _____

3 $27 + 9 =$ _____

4 9, 18, 27, 36, ▢ _____

5 $14 - 9 =$ _____

6 $24 - 9 =$ _____

7 $44 - 9 =$ _____

8 54, 45, 36, 27, ▢ _____

9 ▢ $+ 9 = 15$ _____

10 $12 -$ ▢ $= 9$ _____

C | Answer

1 Add 4 and 9. _____

2 Take 9 from 14. _____

3 The total of 9 and 5 is _____

4 The difference between 12 and 9 is _____

5 The sum of 9 and 8 is _____

6 12 is 9 more than _____

7 Subtract 9 from 13. _____

8 15 minus 9 is _____

9 9 is 7 less than _____

10 9 plus 3 is _____

Mental Arithmetic Introductory Book

A — Answer

1 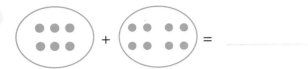 = _____

2  = _____

3  = 3 _____

4 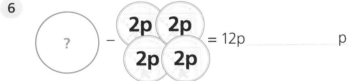 = _____ p

5 = _____ p

6 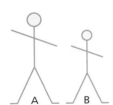 = 12p _____ p

7 Write the name of this shape. _____

8  Which person is taller? _____

9 Which day comes before Thursday? _____

10 What time is it? _____ o'clock

B — Answer

1 5 + 8 = _____

2 15 + 8 = _____

3 35 + 8 = _____

4 8, 16, 24, 32, ___ _____

5 14 − 8 = _____

6 24 − 8 = _____

7 44 − 8 = _____

8 48, 40, 32, 24, ___ _____

9 ___ + 8 = 15 _____

10 12 − ___ = 8 _____

C — Answer

1 Add 7 and 8. _____

2 Take 8 from 14. _____

3 The total of 8 and 4 is _____

4 The difference between 15 and 8 is _____

5 The sum of 8 and 3 is _____

6 12 is 8 more than _____

7 Subtract 8 from 13. _____

8 11 minus 8 is _____

9 8 is 5 less than _____

10 8 plus 6 is _____

9

A | Answer

1 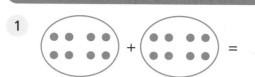 + 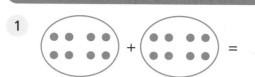 = _____

2 _____ = _____

3 _____ = 4 _____

4  +  = _____ p

5 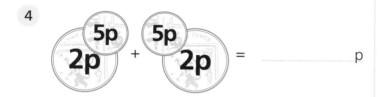 = £ _____

6 (?) − **5p** = 5p _____ p

7 How much is shaded? _____

8 Which glass is half full? _____

9 If today is Monday, what was yesterday? _____

10 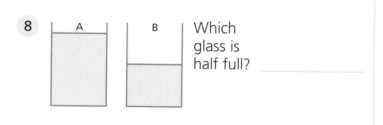 What time is it? _____ o'clock

B | Answer

1   6 + 6 = _____

2   16 + 6 = _____

3   26 + 6 = _____

4   1, 2, 4, 8, ▢ _____

5   16 − 8 = _____

6   26 − 8 = _____

7   36 − 8 = _____

8   16, 8, 4, 2, ▢ _____

9   ▢ + 9 = 18 _____

10   ▢ − 7 = 7 _____

C | Answer

1   Add 8 and 8. _____

2   Take 7 from 14. _____

3   The total of 5 and 5 is _____

4   The difference between 18 and 9 is _____

5   The sum of 6 and 6 is _____

6   8 is 4 more than _____

7   Subtract 5 from 10. _____

8   6 minus 3 is _____

9   7 is 7 less than _____

10   9 plus 9 is _____

Mental Arithmetic Introductory Book

SECTION 1 | Test 8

A

		Answer

1  =

2 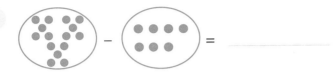 =

3  = 4

4 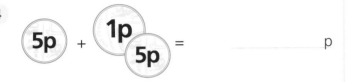 = _____ p

5  = _____ p

6  = 6p _____ p

7 How much is shaded? _____

8 Which door is wider? _____

A   B

9 If today is Wednesday, what was yesterday? _____

10  What time is it? _____ o'clock

B

		Answer

1 3 + 4 =

2 13 + 4 =

3 53 + 4 =

4 3, 7, 11, 15, ▢

5 9 – 4 =

6 19 – 4 =

7 39 – 4 =

8 29, 25, 21, 17, ▢

9 ▢ + 5 = 11

10 ▢ – 7 = 8

C

		Answer

1 Add 6 and 7.

2 Take 9 from 19.

3 The total of 6 and 5 is

4 The difference between 5 and 9 is

5 The sum of 4 and 3 is

6 5 is 2 more than

7 Subtract 7 from 15.

8 17 minus 8 is

9 5 is 6 less than

10 8 plus 7 is

11

A
Answer

1 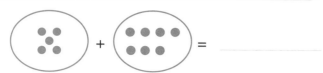 =

2  =

3  = 3

4  = _____ p

5 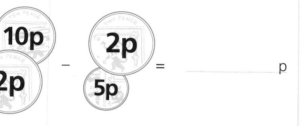 = _____ p

6  = £7 £ _____

7  How much is shaded? _____

8 How much longer is **A** than **B**? _____ cm

A _____ 14cm

B _____ 6cm

9 If today is Friday, what will tomorrow be? _____

10  What time is it? _____ o'clock

B
Answer

1 $5 + 3 =$

2 $15 + 3 =$

3 $35 + 3 =$

4 5, 8, 11, 14, ▢

5 $7 - 5 =$

6 $17 - 5 =$

7 $57 - 5 =$

8 37, 32, 27, 22, ▢

9 ▢ $+ 5 = 8$

10 ▢ $- 7 = 5$

C
Answer

1 Add 6 and 8.

2 Take 9 from 15.

3 The total of 3 and 5 is

4 The difference between 5 and 12 is

5 The sum of 4 and 6 is

6 6 is 2 more than

7 Subtract 7 from 12.

8 18 minus 8 is

9 1 is 3 less than

10 9 plus 7 is

Mental Arithmetic Introductory Book

A   Answer

1 Turn the picture into a sum.   sets of

2 Turn the picture into a sum.   sets of

3  × 6 =

4  ÷ 2 =

5 How much altogether?   £

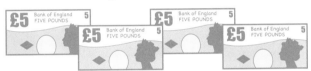

6 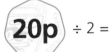 ×   = 10p

7 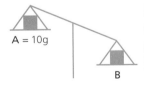 ÷ 2 =   p

8  **B** is twice as heavy as **A**. How heavy is **B**?   g

9 If today is Sunday, what was yesterday?

10 What time is it?   o'clock

B   Answer

1 2, 4, 6, 8,

2 2 + 2 + 2 =

3 3 × 2 =

4 2 + 2 + 2 + 2 + 2 + 2 + 2 =

5 7 × 2 =

6 20, 18, 16,   , 12

7 6 – 2 – 2 – 2 =

8 6 ÷ 2 =

9 14 ÷ 2 =

10 12 ÷ 2 =

C   Answer

1 8 sets of 2 are

2 How many twos in 10?

3 4 twos are

4 How many 2p coins make 20p?

5 9 times 2 is

6 6 multiplied by 2 is

7 8 shared among 2 is

8 Half of 18 is

9 6 divided by 2 is

10 How many socks are there in 10 pairs?

A
Answer

1 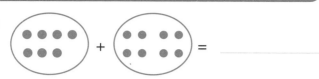 = _____

2 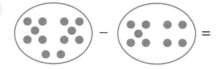 = _____

3 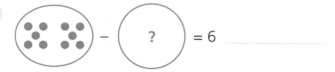 = 6 _____

4  = _____ p

5 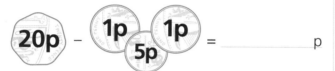 = _____ p

6 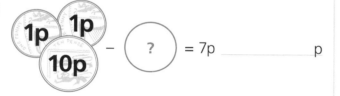 = 7p _____ p

7 Which shape is cut in half? _____

8 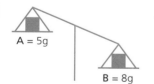 How much heavier is **B**? _____ g

9 If today is Thursday, what will tomorrow be? _____

10  What time is it? _____ o'clock

B
Answer

1 $6 + 7 =$ _____

2 $46 + 7 =$ _____

3 $3 + 9 =$ _____

4 $73 + 9 =$ _____

5 1, 3, 5, 7, ▨ _____

6 $18 - 9 =$ _____

7 $38 - 9 =$ _____

8 $17 - 10 =$ _____

9 $57 - 10 =$ _____

10 19, 17, 15, 13, ▨ _____

C
Answer

1 Add 5 and 8. _____

2 Take 6 from 11. _____

3 The total of 6 and 8 is _____

4 The difference between 13 and 4 is _____

5 The sum of 7 and 5 is _____

6 16 is 9 more than _____

7 Subtract 3 from 7. _____

8 17 minus 9 is _____

9 5 is 3 less than _____

10 7 plus 7 is _____

A   Answer

1   × 2 = _____

2  ÷ 2 = _____

3  − ? = 7 _____

4 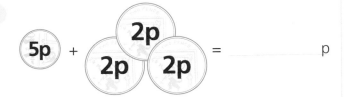 5p + 2p 2p 2p = _____ p

5  £20 − £10 £5 = £ _____

6  2p 2p 2p 2p 2p − ? = 5p _____ p

7 Which shape is cut into quarters? _____

8 A is twice as long as B. How long is A? _____ cm

9 If today is Saturday, what will tomorrow be? _____

10 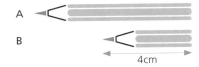 What time is it? _____ o'clock

B   Answer

1 8 + 4 = _____

2 38 + 4 = _____

3 9 − 6 = _____

4 29 − 6 = _____

5 ☐ + 4 = 10 _____

6 ☐ − 9 = 8 _____

7 4, 6, 8, 10, ☐ _____

8 6 × 2 = _____

9 16, 14, 12, 10, ☐ _____

10 18 ÷ 2 = _____

C   Answer

1 9 sets of 2 are _____

2 How many twos in 14? _____

3 The total of 5 and 9 is _____

4 The difference between 6 and 15 is _____

5 The sum of 4 and 8 is _____

6 9 is 4 more than _____

7 Subtract 7 from 16. _____

8 12 shared among 2 is _____

9 9 is 4 less than _____

10 8 multiplied by 2 is _____

15

Name:											
	Achievement Chart for Section 1 Colour the box for each question you got right										
		1	2	3	4	5	6	7	8	9	10
Test 1	Part A										
	Part B										
	Part C										
Test 2	Part A										
	Part B										
	Part C										
Test 3	Part A										
	Part B										
	Part C										
Test 4	Part A										
	Part B										
	Part C										
Test 5	Part A										
	Part B										
	Part C										
Test 6	Part A										
	Part B										
	Part C										
Test 7	Part A										
	Part B										
	Part C										
Test 8	Part A										
	Part B										
	Part C										
Test 9	Part A										
	Part B										
	Part C										
Test 10	Part A										
	Part B										
	Part C										
Test 11	Part A										
	Part B										
	Part C										
Test 12	Part A										
	Part B										
	Part C										

Mental Arithmetic
Introductory Book
Section 2

SECTION 2 | Test 1

A | Answer

1  How many sticks? _____

2  Write the number of cubes in words. _____

3 Draw beads on the abacus to show the number eleven.

tens   units

4 The total value of the money is £11. What is missing? £ _____

5   How much more do you need to make 20p? _____ p

6 You have   . You spend 5p .

How much have you got left? _____ p

7 You have 11p . You buy 9p .

How much change do you get? _____ p

8 You have . You win 5p .

How much do you have now? _____ p

9 Which month comes after March? _____

10  What time is it? _____

B | Answer

1 6 + 10 + 1 = _____

2 16 + 10 + 1 = _____

3 26 + 10 + 1 = _____

4 36 + 11 = _____

5 24 + 11 = _____

6 17 − 10 − 1 = _____

7 27 − 10 − 1 = _____

8 37 − 10 − 1 = _____

9 ☐ − 11 = 46 _____

10 ☐ + 11 = 45 _____

C | Answer

1 Add 7 and 11. _____

2 Take 5 from 11. _____

3 The total of 8 and 11 is _____

4 The difference between 11 and 6 is _____

5 The sum of 11 and 9 is _____

6 11 is 7 more than _____

7 Subtract 9 from 11. _____

8 11 minus 4 is _____

9 8 less than 11 is _____

10 11 plus 6 is _____

A   Answer

1      How many sticks?

2      Write the number of cubes in words.

3   Draw beads on the abacus to show the number twelve.

       tens   units

4   The total value of the coins is 12p. Which coins are missing? _____ p

   ?

5   How much more do you need to make 20p? _____ p

6   You have 12p. You spend 5p.

How much have you got left? _____ p

7   You have  5p 2p 5p. You buy (9p).

How much change do you get? _____ p

8   You have 5p 2p 5p. You win 5p.

How much do you have now? _____ p

9   Which month comes before June? _____

10    What time is it? _____

B   Answer

1   $5 + 10 + 2 =$

2   $15 + 10 + 2 =$

3   $25 + 10 + 2 =$

4   $35 + 12 =$

5   $26 + 12 =$

6   $19 - 10 - 2 =$

7   $29 - 10 - 2 =$

8   $39 - 12 =$

9   ⬜ $- 12 = 49$

10   ⬜ $+ 12 = 47$

C   Answer

1   Add 14 and 12.

2   Take 7 from 12.

3   The total of 9 and 12 is

4   The difference between 12 and 8 is

5   The sum of 12 and 6 is

6   12 is 4 more than

7   Subtract 3 from 12.

8   12 minus 5 is

9   10 less than 12 is

10   12 plus 7 is

A | Answer

1  How many sticks? _____

2 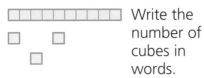 Write the number of cubes in words. _____

3 Draw the beads on the abacus to show the number thirteen.

tens   units

4 The total value of the money is £13. What is missing? £ _____

5 How much more do you need to make 20p? _____ p

6 You have 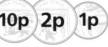 . You spend . How much have you got left? _____ p

7 You have 13p . You buy 9p . How much change do you get? _____ p

8 You have   . You are given 5p . How much do you have now? _____ p

9 Which month comes before January? _____

10  What time is it? _____

B | Answer

1 $4 + 10 + 3 =$ _____

2 $14 + 10 + 3 =$ _____

3 $24 + 13 =$ _____

4 $34 + 13 =$ _____

5 $25 + 13 =$ _____

6 $17 - 10 - 3 =$ _____

7 $27 - 10 - 3 =$ _____

8 $37 - 13 =$ _____

9 $\square - 13 = 43$ _____

10 $\square + 13 = 47$ _____

C | Answer

1 Add 6 and 13. _____

2 Take 4 from 13. _____

3 The total of 5 and 13 is _____

4 The difference between 13 and 8 is _____

5 The sum of 13 and 7 is _____

6 13 is 7 more than _____

7 Subtract 4 from 13. _____

8 13 minus 3 is _____

9 9 less than 13 is _____

10 13 plus 10 is _____

A
Answer

1  How many sticks? _____

2 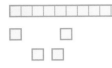 Write the number of cubes in words. _____

3 Draw beads on the abacus to show the number fourteen.

tens   units

4 The total value of the coins is 14p. Which coin is missing? _____ p

5 How much more do you need to make 20p? _____ p

6 You have . You lose 5p.

How much have you got left? _____ p

7 You have 14p. You buy 🧁 9p.

How much change do you get? _____ p

8 You have 10p 2p 2p. You are given 5p.

How much do you have now? _____ p

9 Which month comes after September? _____

10  What time is it? _____

B
Answer

1 $6 + 10 + 4 =$ _____

2 $16 + 14 =$ _____

3 $26 + 14 =$ _____

4 $36 + 14 =$ _____

5 $56 + 14 =$ _____

6 $19 - 10 - 4 =$ _____

7 $29 - 10 - 4 =$ _____

8 $39 - 14 =$ _____

9 ☐ $- 14 = 45$ _____

10 ☐ $+ 14 = 45$ _____

C
Answer

1 Add 5 and 14. _____

2 Take 5 from 14. _____

3 The total of 6 and 14 is _____

4 The difference between 14 and 6 is _____

5 The sum of 14 and 9 is _____

6 14 is 7 more than _____

7 Subtract 9 from 14. _____

8 14 minus 4 is _____

9 8 less than 14 is _____

10 14 plus 3 is _____

A   Answer

1  How many sticks? _____

2 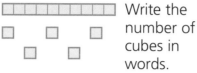 Write the number of cubes in words. _____

3 Draw beads on the abacus to show the number fifteen.

tens   units

4 The total value of the money is £15. What is missing?   £ _____

  ?

5 How much more do you need to make 20p? _____ p

6 You have . You lose .

How much have you got left? _____ p

7 You have 15p . You buy  .

How much change do you get? _____ p

8 You have . You are given .

How much do you have now? _____ p

9 Which month comes after July? _____

10  What time is it? _____

B   Answer

1 $5 + 10 + 5 =$

2 $15 + 15 =$

3 $25 + 15 =$

4 $35 + 15 =$

5 $55 + 15 =$

6 $15 - 10 - 5 =$

7 $25 - 15 =$

8 $35 - 15 =$

9 $\square - 15 = 45$

10 $\square + 15 = 60$

C   Answer

1 Add 10 and 15.

2 Take 7 from 15.

3 The total of 3 and 15 is

4 The difference between 15 and 6 is

5 The sum of 15 and 9 is

6 15 is 5 more than

7 Subtract 9 from 15.

8 15 minus 8 is

9 4 less than 15 is

10 15 plus 6 is

Mental Arithmetic Introductory Book

SECTION 2 | Test 6

A — Answer

1 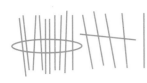 How many sticks? _____

2  Write the number of cubes in words. _____

3 Draw beads on the abacus to show the number sixteen.

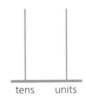

tens   units

4 The total value of the coins is 16p. Which coin is missing? _____ p

5 How much more do you need to make 20p? _____ p

6 You have . You lose 5p. How much have you got left? _____ p

7 You have 16p. You buy 9p. How much change do you get? _____ p

8 You have . You are given 5p. How much do you have now? _____ p

9 Which month comes before October? _____

10  What time is it? _____

B — Answer

1 2 + 10 + 6 = _____

2 12 + 16 = _____

3 22 + 16 = _____

4 32 + 16 = _____

5 52 + 16 = _____

6 18 − 10 − 6 = _____

7 28 − 16 = _____

8 38 − 16 = _____

9 ☐ − 16 = 42 _____

10 ☐ + 16 = 68 _____

C — Answer

1 Add 10 and 16. _____

2 Take 7 from 16. _____

3 The total of 3 and 16 is _____

4 The difference between 16 and 6 is _____

5 The sum of 16 and 9 is _____

6 16 is 5 more than _____

7 Subtract 9 from 16. _____

8 16 minus 8 is _____

9 4 less than 16 is _____

10 16 plus 6 is _____

23

A | Answer

1 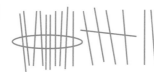 How many sticks? _____

2  Write the number of cubes in words. _____

3 Draw beads on the abacus to show the number seventeen.

tens   units

4 The total value of the coins is 17p. Which coin is missing? _____ p

5 How much more do you need to make 20p? _____ p

6 You have . You lose .

How much have you got left? _____ p

7 You have 17p. You buy 🍎 9p.

How much change do you get? _____ p

8 You have . You are given .

How much do you have now? _____ p

9 Which month comes before April? _____

10  What time is it? _____

B | Answer

1 4 + 10 + 7 = _____

2 14 + 17 = _____

3 24 + 17 = _____

4 34 + 17 = _____

5 54 + 17 = _____

6 20 − 10 − 7 = _____

7 30 − 17 = _____

8 40 − 17 = _____

9 ☐ − 17 = 43 _____

10 ☐ + 17 = 61 _____

C | Answer

1 Add 7 and 17. _____

2 Take 5 from 17. _____

3 The total of 10 and 17 is _____

4 The difference between 17 and 6 is _____

5 The sum of 17 and 9 is _____

6 17 is 7 more than _____

7 Subtract 9 from 17. _____

8 17 minus 4 is _____

9 8 less than 17 is _____

10 17 plus 6 is _____

A   Answer

1    How many sticks? _____

2    Write the number of cubes in words. _____

3   Draw beads on the abacus to show the number eighteen.

tens   units

4   The total value of the coins is 18p. Which coin is missing? _____ p

5   How much more do you need to make 20p? _____ p

6   You have . You spend (5p).

How much have you got left? _____ p

7   You have . You buy [9p] 🍌.

How much change do you get? _____ p

8   You have . You win (5p).

How much do you have now? _____ p

9   Which month comes after November? _____

10    What time is it? _____

B   Answer

1    $4 + 10 + 8 =$ _____

2    $4 + 10 + 10 - 2 =$ _____

3    $24 + 10 + 8 =$ _____

4    $24 + 10 + 10 - 2 =$ _____

5    $24 + 18 =$ _____

6    $20 - 10 - 8 =$ _____

7    $20 - 10 - 10 + 2 =$ _____

8    $20 - 18 =$ _____

9    $\boxed{} - 18 = 42$ _____

10    $\boxed{} + 18 = 42$ _____

C   Answer

1   Increase 10 by 18. _____

2   Take 8 from 18. _____

3   The total of 8 and 18 is _____

4   The difference between 18 and 9 is _____

5   The sum of 18 and 4 is _____

6   18 is 7 more than _____

7   Subtract 6 from 18. _____

8   18 minus 5 is _____

9   3 less than 18 is _____

10   18 plus 2 is _____

SECTION 2 | Test 9

A · Answer

1.  How many sticks? _____

2. 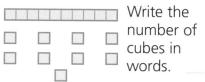 Write the number of cubes in words. _____

3. Draw beads on the abacus to show the number nineteen.

tens   units

4. The total value of the coins is 19p. Which coin is missing? _____ p

5. How much more do you need to make 20p? _____ p

6. You have . You spend 10p. How much have you got left? _____ p

7. You have 19p. You buy _____ 9p. How much change do you get? _____ p

8. You have . You win 10p. How much do you have now? _____ p

9. Which month comes after May? _____

10.  What time is it? _____

B · Answer

1. $3 + 10 + 9 =$ _____

2. $3 + 10 + 10 - 1 =$ _____

3. $23 + 10 + 9 =$ _____

4. $23 + 10 + 10 - 1 =$ _____

5. $23 + 19 =$ _____

6. $40 - 10 - 9 =$ _____

7. $40 - 10 - 10 + 1 =$ _____

8. $40 - 19 =$ _____

9. $\blacksquare - 19 = 41$ _____

10. $\blacksquare + 19 = 41$ _____

C · Answer

1. Add 5 and 19. _____

2. Take 10 from 19. _____

3. The total of 4 and 19 is _____

4. The difference between 19 and 6 is _____

5. The sum of 19 and 9 is _____

6. 19 is 8 more than _____

7. Subtract 6 from 19. _____

8. 19 minus 4 is _____

9. 5 less than 19 is _____

10. 19 plus 3 is _____

A — Answer

1 Turn the picture into a sum. _____ sets of _____

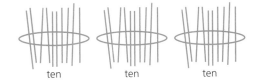
ten   ten   ten

2 Turn the picture into a sum. _____ sets of _____

3 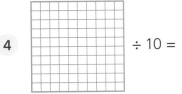 × 10 = _____

4  ÷ 10 = _____

5 How much altogether? _____ p

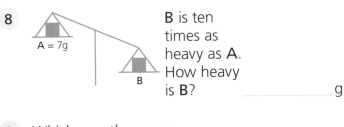

6 10p × ☐ = 70p _____

7 £1 ÷ 10 = _____ p

8
A = 7g
B is ten times as heavy as **A**. How heavy is **B**? _____ g

9 Which month comes after December? _____

10 What time is it? _____

B — Answer

1 10, 20, 30, 40, ☐ _____

2 10 + 10 + 10 = _____

3 3 × 10 = _____

4 10 + 10 + 10 + 10 + 10 = _____

5 5 × 10 = _____

6 90, 80, 70, 60, ☐ _____

7 30 − 10 − 10 − 10 = _____

8 30 ÷ 10 = _____

9 70 ÷ 10 = _____

10 90 ÷ 10 = _____

C — Answer

1 8 sets of 10 are _____

2 How many tens in 70? _____

3 4 tens are _____

4 How many 10p coins make 50p? _____

5 9 times 10 is _____

6 6 multiplied by 10 is _____

7 80 shared among 10 is _____

8 How many 10p coins have the same value as £1? _____

9 60 divided by 10 is _____

10 How many wheels are there altogether on 10 bicycles? _____

A | Answer

1    How many sticks? _____

2    Write the number of cubes in words. _____

3   Draw beads on the abacus to show the number seventeen.

tens   units

4   The total value of the coins is 12p. Which coin is missing? _____ p

5   How much more do you need to make 20p? _____ p
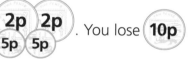

6   You have . You lose 10p.
How much have you got left? _____ p

7   You have 18p. You buy .
How much change do you get? _____ p

8   You have 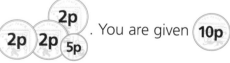. You are given 10p.
How much do you have now? _____ p

9   Which month comes after August? _____

10  What time is it? _____

B | Answer

1   3 + 10 + 5 = _____

2   23 + 15 = _____

3   7 + 10 + 7 = _____

4   47 + 17 = _____

5   16 – 10 – 3 = _____

6   56 – 13 = _____

7   21 – 10 – 6 = _____

8   31 – 16 = _____

9   ▨ – 19 = 4 _____

10 ▨ + 19 = 24 _____

C | Answer

1   Add 9 and 14. _____

2   Take 4 from 19. _____

3   The total of 12 and 3 is _____

4   The difference between 18 and 7 is _____

5   The sum of 11 and 2 is _____

6   17 is 8 more than _____

7   Subtract 4 from 13. _____

8   19 minus 6 is _____

9   5 less than 10 is _____

10 15 plus 5 is _____

A — Answer

1 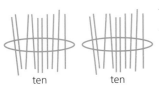 Turn the picture into a sum. _____ sets of _____

2 Write the number of cubes in words. _____

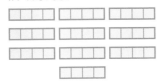

3 Draw beads on the abacus to show the number fourteen.

tens   units

4 The total value of the notes is £60. Which note is missing? £ _____

5 How much more do you need to make 20p? _____ p

6 You have . You spend 10p. How much have you got left? _____ p

7 You have 13p. You buy 8p . How much change do you get? _____ p

8 You have 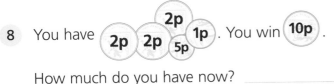. You win 10p. How much do you have now? _____ p

9 Which month comes after February? _____

10  What time is it? _____

B — Answer

1 $4 + 10 + 4 =$ _____

2 $44 + 14 =$ _____

3 $10 + 10 + 10 + 10 =$ _____

4 $4 \times 10 =$ _____

5 $22 - 10 - 7 =$ _____

6 $32 - 17 =$ _____

7 $40 - 10 - 10 - 10 - 10 =$ _____

8 $40 \div 10 =$ _____

9 ☐ $- 18 = 6$ _____

10 ☐ $+ 18 = 26$ _____

C — Answer

1 5 sets of 10 are _____

2 How many tens in 60? _____

3 The total of 5 and 16 is _____

4 The difference between 13 and 7 is _____

5 8 times 10 is _____

6 11 is 8 more than _____

7 Subtract 9 from 14. _____

8 40 divided by 10 is _____

9 3 less than 18 is _____

10 50 shared by 10 is _____

Name:		Achievement Chart for Section 2 Colour the box for each question you got right									
		1	2	3	4	5	6	7	8	9	10
Test 1	Part A										
	Part B										
	Part C										
Test 2	Part A										
	Part B										
	Part C										
Test 3	Part A										
	Part B										
	Part C										
Test 4	Part A										
	Part B										
	Part C										
Test 5	Part A										
	Part B										
	Part C										
Test 6	Part A										
	Part B										
	Part C										
Test 7	Part A										
	Part B										
	Part C										
Test 8	Part A										
	Part B										
	Part C										
Test 9	Part A										
	Part B										
	Part C										
Test 10	Part A										
	Part B										
	Part C										
Test 11	Part A										
	Part B										
	Part C										
Test 12	Part A										
	Part B										
	Part C										

Mental Arithmetic
Introductory Book
Section 3

A · Answer

1 Write the number of sticks in words.

2 Draw beads on the abacus to show the number twenty.

3 Write the number shown on the abacus.

4 How much more do you need to make £1? _____ p

5 How many 10p make 20p ?

6 How many 5p make 20p ?

7 How many 2p make 20p ?

8 What is the difference between **A** and **B**? _____ cm

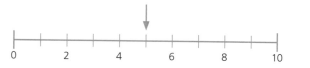

A _____ 20cm
B _____ 12cm

9 What number is the arrow pointing to?

0   2   4   6   8   10

10  What time is it?

B · Answer

1 7 + 10 + 10 = _____

2 17 + 2 tens = _____

3 27 + 20 = _____

4 37 + 20 = _____

5 17, 37, 57, 77, ▮ _____

6 24 − 10 − 10 = _____

7 24 − 2 tens = _____

8 34 − 20 = _____

9 44 − 20 = _____

10 84, 64, 44, ▮, 4 _____

C · Answer

1 Add 7p and 20p. _____ p

2 Take 5p from 20p. _____ p

3 The total cost of 20p and 9p is _____ p

4 The difference in price between 7p and 20p is _____ p

5 The sum of 6p and 20p is _____ p

6 20p is 8p more than _____ p

7 If you spend 10p, your change from 20p is _____ p

8 If you have 20p and you lose 4p, you will be left with _____ p

9 3p less than 20p is _____ p

10 12p plus 20p is _____ p

Mental Arithmetic Introductory Book

SECTION 3 | Test 2

A

Answer

1 Write the number of sticks in words.

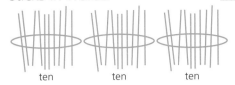

ten　　ten　　ten

2 Draw beads on the abacus to show the number thirty.

h　t　u

3 Write the number shown on the abacus.

h　t　u

4 How much more do you need to make £1?

_____ p

5 How many make ?

6 How many make ?

7 How many make ?

8 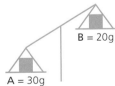 What is the difference in mass between A and B?

B = 20g
A = 30g

_____ g

9 What number is the arrow pointing to?

0　　2　　4　　6　　8　　10

10  What time is it?

B

Answer

1 6 + 10 + 10 + 10 =

2 16 + 3 tens =

3 26 + 30 =

4 36 + 30 =

5 6, 36, 66, ▨ , 126

6 32 − 10 − 10 − 10 =

7 42 − 3 tens =

8 52 − 30 =

9 62 − 30 =

10 122, 92, 62, 32, ▨

C

Answer

1 Add 7cm and 30cm. _____ cm

2 Take 5cm from 30cm. _____ cm

3 The total length of 30cm and 19cm is _____ cm

4 The difference between 7cm and 30cm is _____ cm

5 The sum of 16cm and 30cm is _____ cm

6 30cm is 8cm longer than _____ cm

7 Subtract 11cm from 30cm. _____ cm

8 30cm minus 14cm is _____ cm

9 13cm shorter than 30cm is _____ cm

10 20cm plus 30cm is _____ cm

A   Answer

1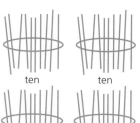
Write the number of sticks in words.

ten   ten   ten   ten

2   Draw beads on the abacus to show the number forty.

h t u

3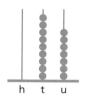
Write the number shown on the abacus.

h t u

4
How much more do you need to make £1?
_____ p

5   How many make  ?

6   How many 5p make 20p 20p ?

7   How many 2p make 20p 20p ?

8   What is the difference between
 20p 20p and 10p ?
_____ p

9   What number is the arrow pointing to?

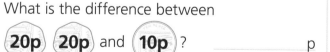
0   2   4   6   8   10

10
What time is it?

B   Answer

1   5 + 10 + 10 + 10 + 10 =

2   15 + 4 tens =

3   25 + 40 =

4   35 + 40 =

5   5, 25, 45, 65, ▨

6   41 − 10 − 10 − 10 − 10 =

7   51 − 4 tens =

8   61 − 40 =

9   71 − 40 =

10 101, 81, 61, 41, ▨

C   Answer

1   Add 7kg and 40kg.   kg

2   Take 5kg from 40kg.   kg

3   The total mass of 40kg and 20kg is   kg

4   The difference between 30kg and 40kg is   kg

5   The sum of 16kg and 40kg is   kg

6   40kg is 8kg heavier than   kg

7   Subtract 11kg from 40kg.   kg

8   40kg minus 4kg is   kg

9   10kg lighter than 40kg is   kg

10 12kg plus 40kg is   kg

A   Answer

1  Write the number of cubes in words. _____

2 Draw beads on the abacus to show the number fifty.

h t u

3 Write the number shown on the abacus. _____

h t u

4 **50p** How much more do you need to make £1? _____ p

5 How many **10p** make **50p** ? _____

6 How many **5p** make **50p** ? _____

7 How many **2p** make **50p** ? _____

8 What is the difference between **A** and **B**? _____ m
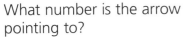
A ——————————— 100m
B ————— 50m

9 What number is the arrow pointing to? _____

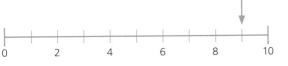

0   2   4   6   8   10

10  What time is it? _____

B   Answer

1   5 + 5 tens = _____

2   15 + 5 tens = _____

3   25 + 50 = _____

4   35 + 50 = _____

5   1, 21, 41, 61, ☐ _____

6   59 − 5 tens = _____

7   69 − 5 tens = _____

8   79 − 50 = _____

9   89 − 50 = _____

10   85, 75, 65, 55, ☐ _____

C   Answer

1   Add £30 and £50.   £ _____

2   Take £5 from £50.   £ _____

3   The total value of £50 and £40 is   £ _____

4   The difference between £20 and £50 is   £ _____

5   The sum of £16 and £50 is   £ _____

6   £50 is £8 more than   £ _____

7   If you spend £15, what is your change from £50?   £ _____

8   £50 minus £40 is   £ _____

9   You have £50. You spend £10. How much have you left?   £ _____

10   £19 plus £50 is   £ _____

A

Answer

1

Write the number of cubes in words.

2 Draw beads on the abacus to show the number sixty.

h   t   u

3
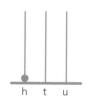
h   t   u
Write the number shown on the abacus.

4

How much more do you need to make £1?

_____ p

5 How many **10p** make **20p 20p 20p** ?

6 How many **5p** make **20p 20p 20p** ?

7 How many **2p** make **20p 20p 20p** ?

8

B = 20kg
A = 60kg
What is the difference in mass between **A** and **B**?

_____ kg

9 What number is the arrow pointing to?

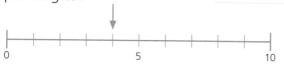
0   5   10

10

What time is it?

B

Answer

1   8 + 6 tens =

2   18 + 6 tens =

3   28 + 60 =

4   38 + 60 =

5   8, 28, 48, 68, ▢

6   60 – 6 tens =

7   70 – 6 tens =

8   80 – 60 =

9   90 – 60 =

10   100, 80, 60, 40, ▢

C

Answer

1   Add 40g and 60g.   _____ g

2   Take 50g from 60g.   _____ g

3   The total value of 60g and 20g is   _____ g

4   The difference between 30g and 60g is   _____ g

5   The sum of 18g and 60g is   _____ g

6   60g is 8g heavier than   _____ g

7   Subtract 11g from 60g.   _____ g

8   60g minus 40g is   _____ g

9   20g lighter than 60g is   _____ g

10   30g plus 60g is   _____ g

A

Answer

1 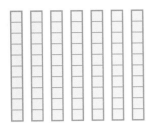 Write the number of cubes in words. _____

2 Draw beads on the abacus to show the number seventy.

h   t   u

3 Write the number shown on the abacus. _____

h   t   u

4  How much more do you need to make £1? _____ p

5 How many make 50p 20p ? _____

6 How many make 50p 20p ? _____

7 How many make 50p 20p ? _____

8 What is the difference between

 ? _____ p

9 What number is the arrow pointing to? _____

0   5   10

10  What time is it? _____

B

Answer

1   10 + 7 tens = _____

2   20 + 7 tens = _____

3   30 + 70 = _____

4   40 + 70 = _____

5   10, 30, 50, 70, ▢ _____

6   80 – 7 tens = _____

7   90 – 7 tens = _____

8   100 – 70 = _____

9   110 – 70 = _____

10 100, 90, 80, 70, ▢ _____

C

Answer

1   Add 30m and 70m. _____ m

2   Take 40m from 70m. _____ m

3   The total length of 70m and 20m is _____ m

4   The difference between 7m and 70m is _____ m

5   The sum of 16m and 70m is _____ m

6   70m is 20m longer than _____ m

7   Subtract 50m from 70m. _____ m

8   70m minus 60m is _____ m

9   8m shorter than 70m is _____ m

10 19m plus 70m is _____ m

Schofield & Sims

A | Answer

1 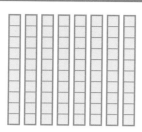 Write the number of cubes in words. _____

2 Draw beads on the abacus to show the number eighty.

h   t   u

3 Write the number shown on the abacus. _____

h   t   u

4 How much more do you need to make £1? _____ p

5 How many make ? _____

6 How many make ? _____

7 How many make 20p 20p 20p 20p? _____

8 What is the difference between and [image] ? _____ litres

9 What number is the arrow pointing to? _____

0   5   10

10  What time is it? _____

B | Answer

1   10 + 8 tens = _____

2   20 + 8 tens = _____

3   30 + 80 = _____

4   40 + 80 = _____

5   0, 30, 60, 90, ▢ _____

6   80 – 8 tens = _____

7   90 – 8 tens = _____

8   100 – 80 = _____

9   110 – 80 = _____

10 101, 91, 81, 71, ▢ _____

C | Answer

1   Add 19m and 80m. _____ m

2   Take 60m from 80m. _____ m

3   The total length of 80m and 15m is _____ m

4   The difference between 70m and 80m is _____ m

5   The sum of 6m and 80m is _____ m

6   80m is 30m longer than _____ m

7   Subtract 20m from 80m. _____ m

8   80m minus 40m is _____ m

9   30m shorter than 80m is _____ m

10 8m plus 80m is _____ m

Mental Arithmetic Introductory Book

SECTION 3 | Test 8

A   Answer

1 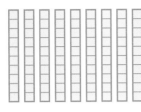 Write the number of cubes in words. _____

2 Draw beads on the abacus to show the number ninety.

3 Write the number shown on the abacus. _____

4  How much more do you need to make £1? _____ p

5 How many make  ? _____

6 How many make  ? _____

7 How many make  ? _____

8 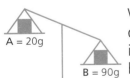 What is the difference in mass between **A** and **B**? _____ g

9 What number is the arrow pointing to? _____

10  What time is it? _____

B   Answer

1 10 + 9 tens = _____

2 20 + 9 tens = _____

3 30 + 90 = _____

4 40 + 90 = _____

5 0, 25, 50, 75, ▢ _____

6 100 – 9 tens = _____

7 110 – 9 tens = _____

8 120 – 90 = _____

9 130 – 90 = _____

10 105, 85, 65, 45, ▢ _____

C   Answer

1 Add 9min and 90min. _____ min

2 Take 50min from 90min. _____ min

3 The total time taken for two TV programmes lasting 90min and 20min is _____ min

4 The difference between 60min and 90min is _____ min

5 The sum of 6min and 90min is _____ min

6 90min is 5min longer than _____ min

7 Subtract 15min from 90min. _____ min

8 90min minus 40min is _____ min

9 30min less than 90min is _____ min

10 8min plus 90min is _____ min

39

A   Answer

1 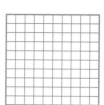 Write the number of cubes in words. _____

2 Draw beads on the abacus to show the number one hundred.
h   t   u

3 Write the number shown on the abacus. _____
h   t   u

4 How much more do you need to make £1? _____ p

5 How many make ? _____

6 How many make ? _____

7 How many make ? _____

8 What is the difference between
 and ? _____ ml

9 What number is the arrow pointing to? _____

0   5   10

10  What time is it? _____

B   Answer

1   10 + 10 tens = _____

2   20 + 1 hundred = _____

3   30 + 100 = _____

4   40 + 100 = _____

5   0, 100, 200, 300, ▓ _____

6   100 – 10 tens = _____

7   110 – 1 hundred = _____

8   120 – 100 = _____

9   130 – 100 = _____

10 900, 800, 700, 600, ▓ _____

C   Answer

1   Add 7 tens and 10 tens. _____

2   Take 5 tens from 10 tens. _____

3   The total of 10 tens and 9 tens is _____

4   The difference between 7 tens and 10 tens is _____

5   The sum of 6 tens and 10 tens is _____

6   10 tens are 8 tens more than _____

7   Subtract 1 ten from 10 tens. _____

8   10 tens minus 4 tens is _____

9   3 tens fewer than 10 tens is _____

10 2 tens plus 10 tens is _____

A
Answer

1 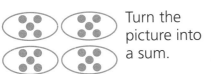 Turn the picture into a sum. _____ sets of _____

2 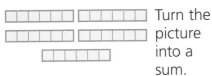 Turn the picture into a sum. _____ sets of _____

3  × 5 = _____

4  ÷ 5 = _____

5 How much altogether? _____ p

6 × ▨ = 40p _____

7 20p ÷ 5 = _____ p

8 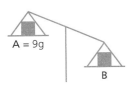 B is five times as heavy as A. How heavy is B? _____ g

A = 9g

9 What number is the arrow pointing to? _____

10 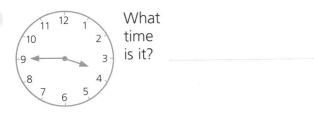 What time is it? _____

B
Answer

1 5, 10, 15, 20, ▨ _____

2 5 + 5 + 5 + 5 = _____

3 4 × 5 = _____

4 5 + 5 + 5 + 5 + 5 + 5 = _____

5 6 × 5 = _____

6 50, 45, 40, 35, ▨ _____

7 15 − 5 − 5 − 5 = _____

8 15 ÷ 5 = _____

9 35 ÷ 5 = _____

10 40 ÷ 5 = _____

C
Answer

1 8 sets of 5 are _____

2 How many fives in 30? _____

3 9 fives are _____

4 How many 5p coins make 50p? _____

5 7 times 5 is _____

6 6 multiplied by 5 is _____

7 40 shared among 5 is _____

8 If I change 20p into 5p coins, how many will I get? _____

9 45 divided by 5 is _____

10 How many toes are there on 10 feet? _____

A   Answer

1 Write the number of cubes
   in words.

_____

2 Draw beads on the abacus to
   show the number sixty-four.

h t u

3
   Write the number
   shown on
   the abacus.   _____

   h t u

4 **50p 10p 10p**   How much
                      more do
                      you need
                      to make £1?   _____ p

5 How many **10p** make **20p 20p 20p 20p** ?   _____

6 How many **5p** make **10p 10p** ?   _____

7 How many **2p** make **10p 10p 20p** ?   _____

8 What is the difference between

   £1 and **50p** ?   _____ p

9 What number is the arrow
   pointing to?   _____

0   10

10    What
                           time
                           is it?   _____

B   Answer

1   5 + 5 tens =   _____

2   35 + 50 =   _____

3   3 + 7 tens =   _____

4   23 + 70 =   _____

5   3, 23, 43, 63, ▢   _____

6   78 – 3 tens =   _____

7   98 – 30 =   _____

8   90 – 4 tens =   _____

9   60 – 40 =   _____

10 87, 77, 67, 57, ▢   _____

C   Answer

1   Add 50cm and 60cm.   _____ cm

2   Take 70 litres from 80 litres. _____ litres

3   The total mass of four boxes
    each weighing 10kg is   _____ kg

4   The difference in value
    between 80p and 30p is   _____ p

5   The sum of 100g and 90g is   _____ g

6   100 is 5 tens more than   _____

7   Subtract 30ml from 40ml.   _____ ml

8   80min minus 50min is   _____ min

9   70m is 10m shorter than   _____ m

10 £60 plus £20 is   £ _____

A | Answer

1 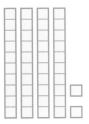 Write the number of cubes in words.

2 Draw beads on the abacus to show the number thirty-five.

h t u

3 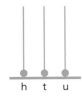 Write the number shown on the abacus.

h t u

4 How much more do you need to make £1? _____ p

5 How many  ?

6 How many ?

7 How many **2p** make **10p 20p 20p** ?

8 What is the difference in width between **A** and **B**? _____ cm

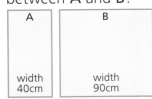
A width 40cm   B width 90cm

9 What number is the arrow pointing to?

0   10

10  What time is it?

B | Answer

1 4 + 8 tens =

2 24 + 80 =

3 6 + 2 tens =

4 76 + 20 =

5 5, 105, 205, 305,

6 87 – 6 tens =

7 67 – 60 =

8 99 – 3 tens =

9 69 – 3 tens =

10 200, 150, 100,

C | Answer

1 On Tuesday a farmer adds 40 litres of milk to 10 litres he got on Monday. How much has he got now? _____ litres

2 If I take £20 from my savings of £80, how much is left? £ _____

3 The total length of two sticks measuring 70cm and 60cm is _____ cm

4 The difference in price between two comics costing 90p and 30p is _____ p

5 The sum of two loads with masses 50kg and 60kg is _____ kg

6 A 100ml bottle of water has 10ml more than one which contains _____ ml

7 If I cut off 30m from a 90m length of rope, how much is left? _____ m

8 If 7g of a 100g packet of sweets is the wrapper, how much do the sweets weigh? _____ g

9 I scored 2 tens less than Leo who scored 5 tens. What was my score?

10 The time taken for a football match was 40min plus 10min half time. How long did it take altogether? _____ min

Name:		Achievement Chart for Section 3 Colour the box for each question you got right									
		1	2	3	4	5	6	7	8	9	10
Test 1	Part A										
	Part B										
	Part C										
Test 2	Part A										
	Part B										
	Part C										
Test 3	Part A										
	Part B										
	Part C										
Test 4	Part A										
	Part B										
	Part C										
Test 5	Part A										
	Part B										
	Part C										
Test 6	Part A										
	Part B										
	Part C										
Test 7	Part A										
	Part B										
	Part C										
Test 8	Part A										
	Part B										
	Part C										
Test 9	Part A										
	Part B										
	Part C										
Test 10	Part A										
	Part B										
	Part C										
Test 11	Part A										
	Part B										
	Part C										
Test 12	Part A										
	Part B										
	Part C										

DOUBLES

1 + 1 =	2 − 1 =
2 + 2 =	4 − 2 =
3 + 3 =	6 − 3 =
4 + 4 =	8 − 4 =
5 + 5 =	10 − 5 =
6 + 6 =	12 − 6 =
7 + 7 =	14 − 7 =
8 + 8 =	16 − 8 =
9 + 9 =	18 − 9 =
10 + 10 =	20 − 10 =

NEAR DOUBLES

1 + 2 =	2 + 1 =	3 − 1 =	3 − 2 =
2 + 3 =	3 + 2 =	5 − 2 =	5 − 3 =
3 + 4 =	4 + 3 =	7 − 3 =	7 − 4 =
4 + 5 =	5 + 4 =	9 − 4 =	9 − 5 =
5 + 6 =	6 + 5 =	11 − 5 =	11 − 6 =
6 + 7 =	7 + 6 =	13 − 6 =	13 − 7 =
7 + 8 =	8 + 7 =	15 − 7 =	15 − 8 =
8 + 9 =	9 + 8 =	17 − 8 =	17 − 9 =

NEAR NEAR DOUBLES

1 + 3 =	3 + 1 =	4 − 1 =	4 − 3 =
2 + 4 =	4 + 2 =	6 − 2 =	6 − 4 =
3 + 5 =	5 + 3 =	8 − 3 =	8 − 5 =
4 + 6 =	6 + 4 =	10 − 4 =	10 − 6 =
5 + 7 =	7 + 5 =	12 − 5 =	12 − 7 =
6 + 8 =	8 + 6 =	14 − 6 =	14 − 8 =
7 + 9 =	9 + 7 =	16 − 7 =	16 − 9 =
8 + 10 =	10 + 8 =	18 − 8 =	18 − 10 =

Schofield & Sim

COUNTING ON 1 and related facts

1 + 1 =	1 + 1 =	2 – 1 =	2 – 1 =
2 + 1 =	1 + 2 =	3 – 1 =	3 – 2 =
3 + 1 =	1 + 3 =	4 – 1 =	4 – 3 =
4 + 1 =	1 + 4 =	5 – 1 =	5 – 4 =
5 + 1 =	1 + 5 =	6 – 1 =	6 – 5 =
6 + 1 =	1 + 6 =	7 – 1 =	7 – 6 =
7 + 1 =	1 + 7 =	8 – 1 =	8 – 7 =
8 + 1 =	1 + 8 =	9 – 1 =	9 – 8 =
9 + 1 =	1 + 9 =	10 – 1 =	10 – 9 =

COUNTING ON 2 and related facts

1 + 2 =	2 + 1 =	3 – 2 =	3 – 1 =
2 + 2 =	2 + 2 =	4 – 2 =	4 – 2 =
3 + 2 =	2 + 3 =	5 – 2 =	5 – 3 =
4 + 2 =	2 + 4 =	6 – 2 =	6 – 4 =
5 + 2 =	2 + 5 =	7 – 2 =	7 – 5 =
6 + 2 =	2 + 6 =	8 – 2 =	8 – 6 =
7 + 2 =	2 + 7 =	9 – 2 =	9 – 7 =
8 + 2 =	2 + 8 =	10 – 2 =	10 – 8 =
9 + 2 =	2 + 9 =	11 – 2 =	11 – 9 =

ADDING 10 and related facts

1 + 10 =	10 + 1 =	11 – 10 =	11 – 1 =
2 + 10 =	10 + 2 =	12 – 10 =	12 – 2 =
3 + 10 =	10 + 3 =	13 – 10 =	13 – 3 =
4 + 10 =	10 + 4 =	14 – 10 =	14 – 4 =
5 + 10 =	10 + 5 =	15 – 10 =	15 – 5 =
6 + 10 =	10 + 6 =	16 – 10 =	16 – 6 =
7 + 10 =	10 + 7 =	17 – 10 =	17 – 7 =
8 + 10 =	10 + 8 =	18 – 10 =	18 – 8 =
9 + 10 =	10 + 9 =	19 – 10 =	19 – 9 =

MAKING 10 and related facts

1 + 9 =	9 + 1 =	10 − 1 =	10 − 9 =
2 + 8 =	8 + 2 =	10 − 2 =	10 − 8 =
3 + 7 =	7 + 3 =	10 − 3 =	10 − 7 =
4 + 6 =	6 + 4 =	10 − 4 =	10 − 6 =
5 + 5 =	5 + 5 =	10 − 5 =	10 − 5 =

ADDING 9 and related facts

1 + 9 =	9 + 1 =	10 − 9 =	10 − 1 =
2 + 9 =	9 + 2 =	11 − 9 =	11 − 2 =
3 + 9 =	9 + 3 =	12 − 9 =	12 − 3 =
4 + 9 =	9 + 4 =	13 − 9 =	13 − 4 =
5 + 9 =	9 + 5 =	14 − 9 =	14 − 5 =
6 + 9 =	9 + 6 =	15 − 9 =	15 − 6 =
7 + 9 =	9 + 7 =	16 − 9 =	16 − 7 =
8 + 9 =	9 + 8 =	17 − 9 =	17 − 8 =
9 + 9 =	9 + 9 =	18 − 9 =	18 − 9 =

ADDING 8 and related facts

1 + 8 =	8 + 1 =	9 − 8 =	9 − 1 =
2 + 8 =	8 + 2 =	10 − 8 =	10 − 2 =
3 + 8 =	8 + 3 =	11 − 8 =	11 − 3 =
4 + 8 =	8 + 4 =	12 − 8 =	12 − 4 =
5 + 8 =	8 + 5 =	13 − 8 =	13 − 5 =
6 + 8 =	8 + 6 =	14 − 8 =	14 − 6 =
7 + 8 =	8 + 7 =	15 − 8 =	15 − 7 =
8 + 8 =	8 + 8 =	16 − 8 =	16 − 8 =
9 + 8 =	8 + 9 =	17 − 8 =	17 − 9 =

Schofield&Sims

the long-established educational publisher specialising in maths, English and science

Mental Arithmetic provides rich and varied practice to meet the requirements of the National Curriculum for primary mathematics. The **Mental Arithmetic Introductory Book** acts as a bridge from Key Stage 1, covering all four number operations, as well as sequences and simple money problems. The accompanying answer book, **Mental Arithmetic Introductory Book Answers**, has increased diagnostic support, making it particularly useful for monitoring children with special educational needs.

Mental Arithmetic comprises seven one-per-child pupil books with accompanying answer books, as well as a single Teacher's Guide. The series develops pupils' essential maths skills, preparing them for the Key Stage 2 national tests. It may also be used as preparation for the 11+, and with older students for consolidation and recovery. All the books can be used flexibly for individual, paired, group or whole-class maths practice, as well as for homework and one-to-one intervention.

Structured according to ability rather than age, the series allows children to work at their own pace, building confidence and fluency. Two **Entry Tests** are available in the **Mental Arithmetic Teacher's Guide** and on the Schofield & Sims website, enabling teachers, parents and tutors to select the appropriate book for each child.

The **Mental Arithmetic Introductory Book** contains:

* 36 one-page tests, each comprising the following three parts

  Part A: questions using pictures to develop basic maths skills

  Part B: questions using symbols and patterns

  Part C: questions using simple and consistent language
* **Achievement Charts** to monitor progress as pupils work through the book
* **Just Facts** questions to provide additional practice of key maths facts.

Mental Arithmetic Introductory Book 978 07217 0798 3	**Mental Arithmetic Introductory Book Answers** 978 07217 0853 9
Mental Arithmetic 1 978 07217 0799 0	**Mental Arithmetic 1 Answers** 978 07217 0805 8
Mental Arithmetic 2 978 07217 0800 3	**Mental Arithmetic 2 Answers** 978 07217 0806 5
Mental Arithmetic 3 978 07217 0801 0	**Mental Arithmetic 3 Answers** 978 07217 0807 2
Mental Arithmetic 4 978 07217 0802 7	**Mental Arithmetic 4 Answers** 978 07217 0808 9
Mental Arithmetic 5 978 07217 0803 4	**Mental Arithmetic 5 Answers** 978 07217 0809 6
Mental Arithmetic 6 978 07217 0804 1	**Mental Arithmetic 6 Answers** 978 07217 0810 2
Mental Arithmetic Teacher's Guide 978 07217 1389 2	

First Mental Arithmetic is available for younger pupils

This edition copyright © Schofield & Sims Ltd, 2016. Fourth impression 2016.
First edition published in 1995, compiled by Lynn Spavin
British Library Cataloguing in Publication Data. A catalogue record for this book is available from the British Library.
Design by Ledgard Jepson Ltd. Front cover design by Peter Grundy. Printed in the UK by Page Bros (Norwich) Ltd.

Mental Arithmetic

MIX
Paper from responsible sources
FSC® C023114

ISBN 978-07217-0798-3

9 780721 707983

ISBN 978 07217 0798 3
Key Stage 2
Age range 7–11+ years
£3.50 (Retail price)

For further information and to place your order visit
www.schofieldandsims.co.uk or telephone 01484 607080